DOODLE TIME

Draw the Bat-Signal in the sky.

NIGHT VISION

When you're patrolling the streets of Gotham City at night, it's important that you have excellent night vision. How many times can you spot the Batman logo on this page?

See answer on page 32

SYMBOL SKETCH

If you were a vigilante crime fighter, what would your symbol be? Design one here!

Batman created by Bob Kane with Bill Finger.
Superman created by Jerry Siegel and Joe Shuster. By special arrangement with the Jerry Siegel family.
Wonder Woman created by William Moulton Marston.

This book belongs to:

TOby garner

There is a secret phrase hidden throughout this book. Find the letters and unscramble them to make the secret code phrase.

Letters found:

Code phrase:

BATMAN v SUPERMAN™: ULTIMATE STICKER BOOK
A CENTUM BOOK 9781910916131
Published in Great Britain by Centum Books Ltd
This edition published 2016
1 3 5 7 9 10 8 6 4 2

Centum Books Ltd, 20 Devon Square, Newton Abbot, Devon, TQ12 2HR, UK
books@centumbooksltd.co.uk
CENTUM BOOKS Limited Reg. No. 07641486
A CIP catalogue record for this book is available from the British Library
Printed in Italy

THE DARK KNIGHT

Real name:
Bruce Wayne

Lives:
Wayne Manor, Gotham City

Powers:
Superior intellect, martial arts, World's Greatest Detective

Gadgets:
Batarangs, grapnel guns, Utility Belt

Vehicles:
Batmobile, Batwing

The coolest thing about Batman is:

_ _

_ _

I think Batman is the symbol Gotham City needs because:

_ _

_ _

If I could design a gadget for Batman it would be:

_ _

_ _

BATMAN'S SUIT

Batman's suit is what hides his true identity, whilst inspiring fear in all of Gotham City's villains. He also wears a Utility Belt that is packed with awesome gadgets. Design a new suit for Batman below.

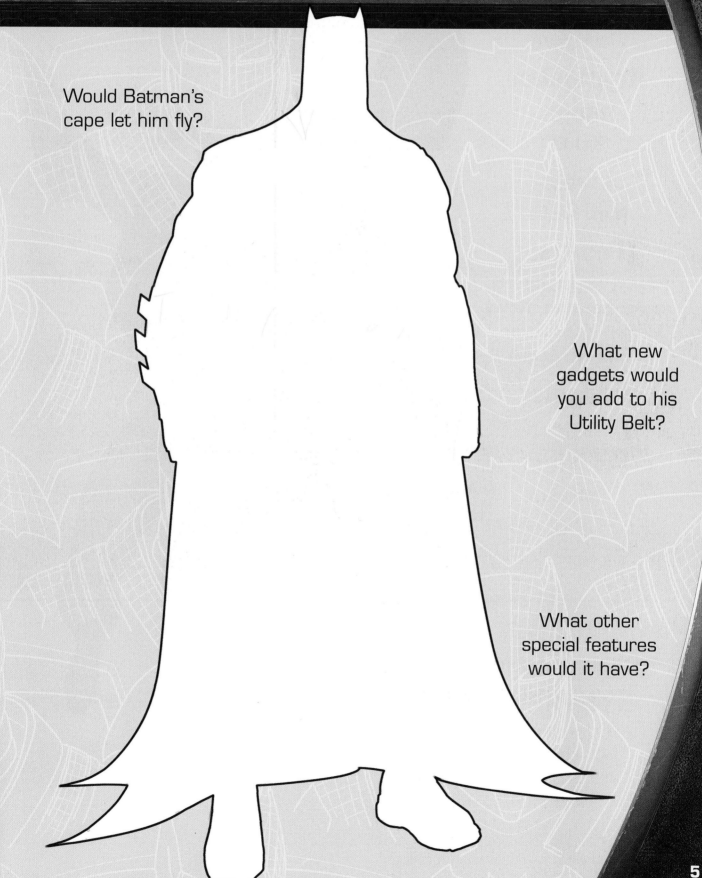

Would Batman's cape let him fly?

What new gadgets would you add to his Utility Belt?

What other special features would it have?

THE MAN OF STEEL

Earth name:
Clark Kent

Kryptonian name:
Kal-El

Lives:
Metropolis

Powers:
Flight, super-speed, super-hearing, X-ray vision, heat vision, super-strength

Gadgets:
None

Vehicles:
None

The coolest thing about Superman is:

_____

_____

I think Superman is a great super hero because:

_____

_____

If I met Superman, I would ask him to:

_____

_____

Draw Superman flying over Metropolis.

SPOT SUPERMAN

There's only one Superman – can you find the only Superman below with no differences to this image?

1.

2.

3.

4.

5.

6.

See answer on page 32

SYMBOL SKETCH
Draw Superman's symbol here.

SUPERMAN'S SUPERPOWERS

Superman has to choose which superpower to use in every dangerous situation. Can you match his superpower to the situation?

POWERS

- Super-strength
- Super-speed
- X-ray vision
- Flight

SITUATION

a) Broken bridge

A railway bridge has broken, and a train is heading towards it. How will Superman save all the train passengers?

b) Emergency

There's a crime happening downtown, Superman has to get there . . . and fast! How will he get there in time?

c) Tall building

Someone is trapped at the top of a tall building. How would Superman get to the top?

d) Building collapse

A building has collapsed, and there are people trapped underneath. How will Superman find out where they are?

See answers on page 32

The entire car is thickly armoured to keep Batman safe

Tyres are bulletproof and fireproof

The Batmobile is equipped with a wide range of non-lethal weapons

DOODLE TIME

Design your own vehicle for Batman below.

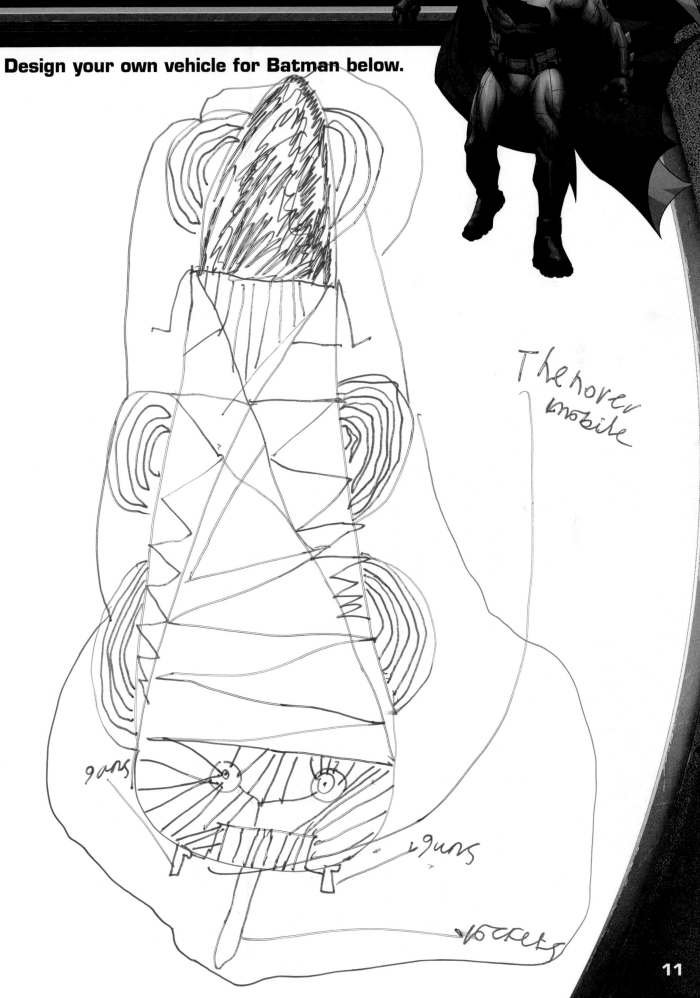

The hover mobile

guns

guns

rockets

WONDER WOMAN

Real name:
Diana Prince

Lives:
Unknown

Powers:
Wisdom, super-strength

Gadgets:
Sword, Shield, Lasso

Vehicles:
None

The coolest thing about Wonder Woman is:

_____

_____

I think Wonder Woman is a great super hero because:

_____

_____

_____

If I could design a gadget for Wonder Woman it would be:

_____

_____

_____

Draw Wonder Woman fighting bad guys below.

Amy

WONDER WOMAN'S LASSO

Wonder Woman's lasso can always capture the villain.
Follow the lasso tangle to find out where Wonder Woman
is going.

See answer on page 32

1.
2.
3.
4.

GOTHAM CITY

WORD LASSO

Can you find five words hiding in Wonder Woman's lasso that help to create her power? The words may be forwards or backwards.

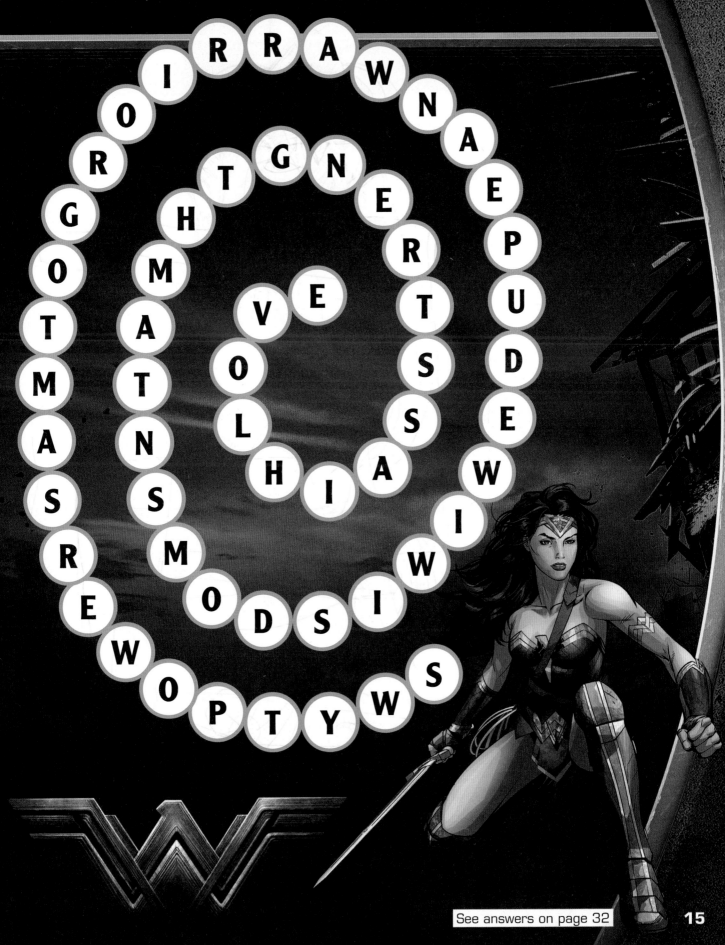

See answers on page 32

COMIC STRIP DOODLE

When Batman and Superman finally go face-to-face – who knows what will happen! Are they friends? Are they enemies? Doodle and sketch what you think happens below.
Use your stickers to help you.

SUPER HERO WORDSEARCH

Can you find all these words in the grid below?

SUPERMAN
BATMAN ✓
WONDER WOMAN
LEX LUTHOR ✓

ALIEN ✓
BATMOBILE ✓
VIGILANTE ✓
SAVIOUR ✓

GOTHAM CITY ✓
CLARK KENT ✓
BRUCE WAYNE ✓

See answers on page 32

H	E	R	O	R	V	I	G	I	L	A	N	T	E
E	G	O	T	U	H	A	H	M	C	H	E	R	O
R	N	A	M	O	W	R	E	D	N	O	W	V	I
O	S	U	P	I	E	R	R	M	A	N	I	E	G
C	R	B	A	V	T	M	O	N	A	N	L	L	R
N	A	E	L	A	H	I	A	L	I	E	N	I	O
A	B	A	H	S	E	M	L	E	X	L	U	B	H
M	T	C	L	A	R	K	K	E	N	T	A	O	T
T	M	O	B	E	O	O	I	L	E	T	N	M	U
A	D	N	P	E	R	R	H	E	R	O	O	T	L
B	R	U	C	E	W	A	Y	N	E	E	W	A	X
Q	S	C	H	L	A	R	M	K	R	N	Y	B	E
W	G	O	T	H	A	M	C	I	T	Y	G	L	L

How many times can you find 'HERO' hidden in the grid?

SPOT THE DIFFERENCE

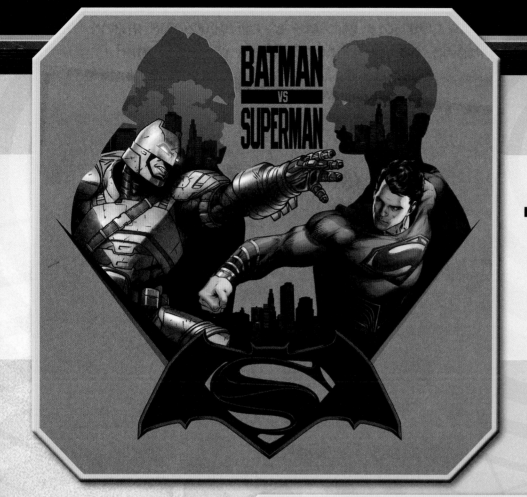

A super hero needs a keen eye to spot danger. Can you spot 15 differences between these 2 pictures?

See answers on page 32

CRIME FIGHTER PUZZLE

To fight crime and deal out justice, you sometimes need to solve puzzles. Use your stickers to complete the puzzle. Some are missing, so you'll have to draw them instead.

SUPER HERO SEQUENCES

Can you complete these sequences using your stickers?

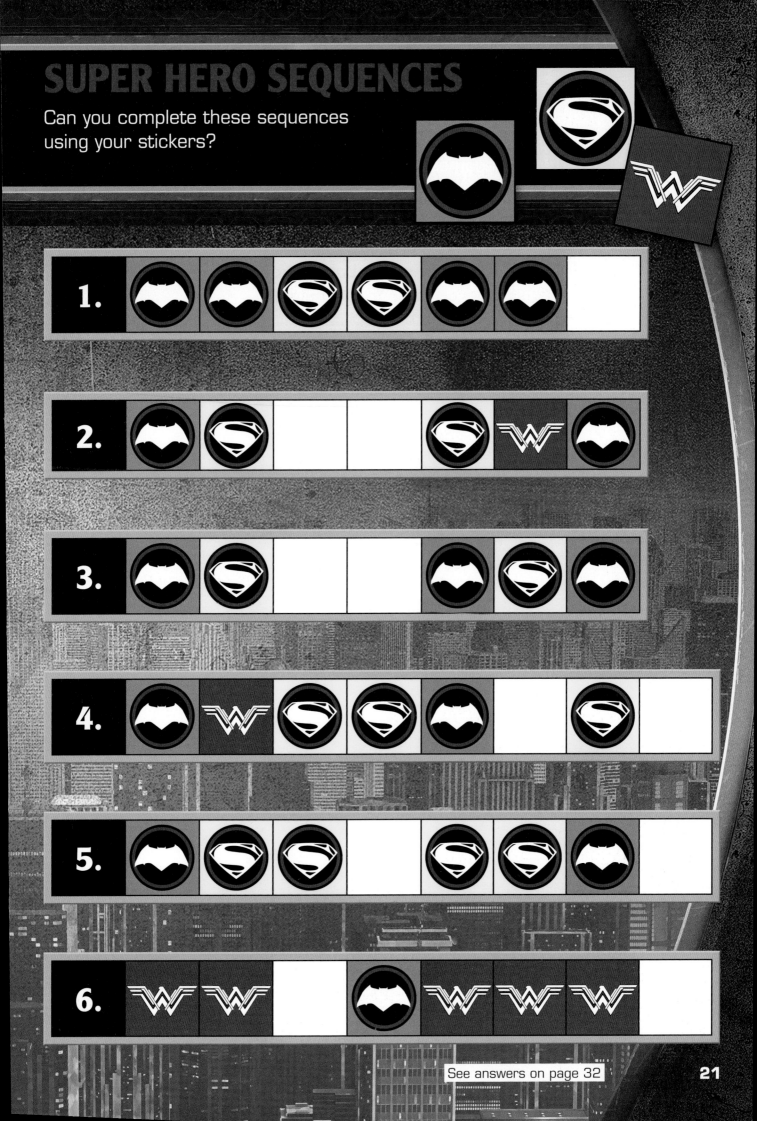

See answers on page 32

DOODLE

The symbols of Batman and Superman are iconic – just the sight of them makes evil-doers tremble in fear! By combining them together, it becomes a symbol which inspires twice as much fear.

How many ways can you think to combine both logos? Sketch your ideas below.

SUPERPOWERED WORD GRID

We use many different words to describe our heroes. Can you fit all the words below into the grid? Watch out – some words have the same number of letters and may fit into more than one space!

WORDS TO FIT:

STRONGEST

BRAVEST

FASTEST

WARRIOR

SAVIOUR

GUARDIAN

See answers on page 32

START ▶▶

1.

2. **TURN LEFT OR RIGHT** ◀◀ ▶▶

3.

3.

4.

5. **Wonder Woman is here! Go forward five spaces.**

6.

7.

8. **Shout out your favourite super hero's name or miss a turn.**

9.

10.

11. **Lex Luthor has an evil plan. Miss a turn.**

12.

13.

4. **Superman soars through the sky. Go forward three spaces.**

5.

6.

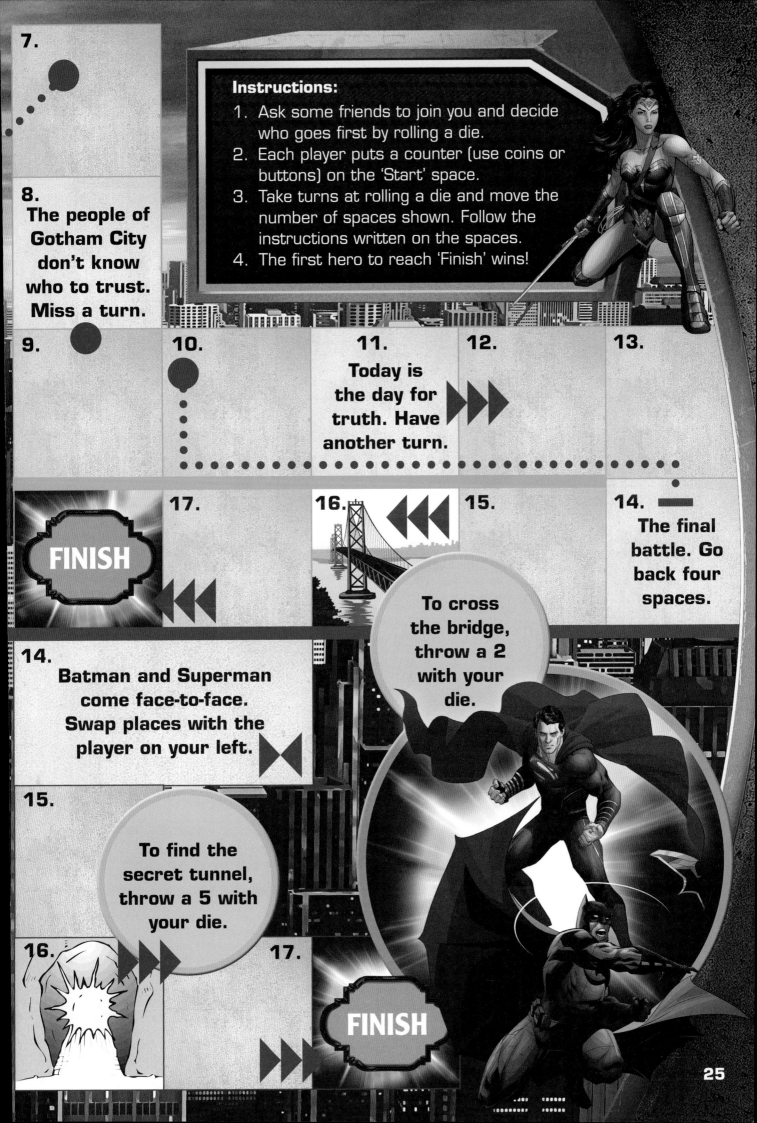

7.

8. The people of Gotham City don't know who to trust. Miss a turn.

Instructions:
1. Ask some friends to join you and decide who goes first by rolling a die.
2. Each player puts a counter (use coins or buttons) on the 'Start' space.
3. Take turns at rolling a die and move the number of spaces shown. Follow the instructions written on the spaces.
4. The first hero to reach 'Finish' wins!

9.

10.

11. Today is the day for truth. Have another turn.

12.

13.

14. The final battle. Go back four spaces.

15.

16. To cross the bridge, throw a 2 with your die.

17.

FINISH

14. Batman and Superman come face-to-face. Swap places with the player on your left.

15. To find the secret tunnel, throw a 5 with your die.

16.

17.

FINISH

SECRET DECODER

When a city doesn't know who to trust, there's only one way to pass messages . . . secretly! Can you decode the super secret message below?

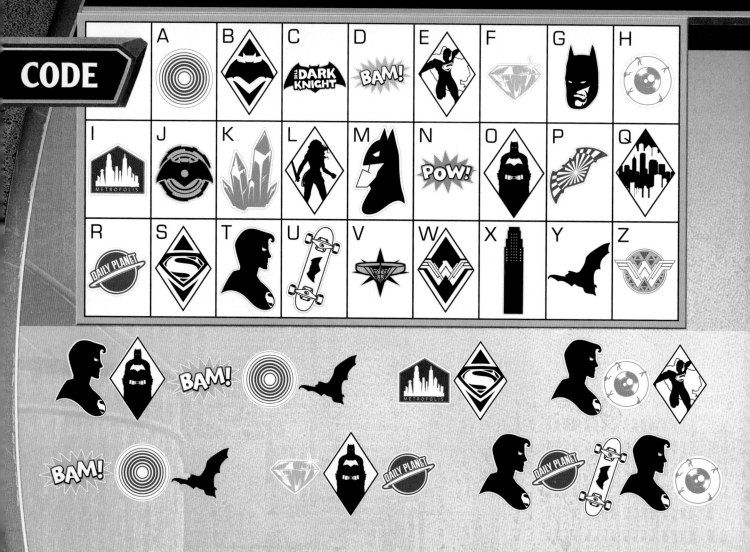

CODE

Now use the code to create your own secret message.
Draw the symbols for each letter of your message here.

COPY AND DRAW!

Can you copy this image of Batman and Superman into the grid below?

Don't forget to colour your picture in!

FILL IN THE GAPS NEWSPAPER STORY

DAILY PLANET

MONDAY

TUESDAY

It's been a big week of news at the *Daily Planet*. Write a headline for each day of the week. Don't forget to draw the front page photo too.

WEDNESDAY

- -

- -

- -

- -

- -

- -

THURSDAY

- -

- -

- -

- -

- -

- -

FRIDAY

- -

- -

- -

- -

- -

ULTIMATE HERO CHALLENGE

It's time to see if you are ready for the tough world of crime fighting. If you can complete all the activities on the page, perhaps you're ready to become the symbol Gotham City needs.

1.

Can you complete this tricky Sudoku puzzle? Each image needs to appear on each row, column and box only once.

BAM!

2.

T	R	U	T	H
R	R	T	T	R
U	U	U	U	U
T	R	H	T	T
T	R	U	T	H

How man times can you find 'truth' in the grid below?

COPY AND DRAW!

Can you copy this image of Batman and Superman
into the grid below?

Don't forget to colour your picture in!

DAILY PLANET

MONDAY

TUESDAY

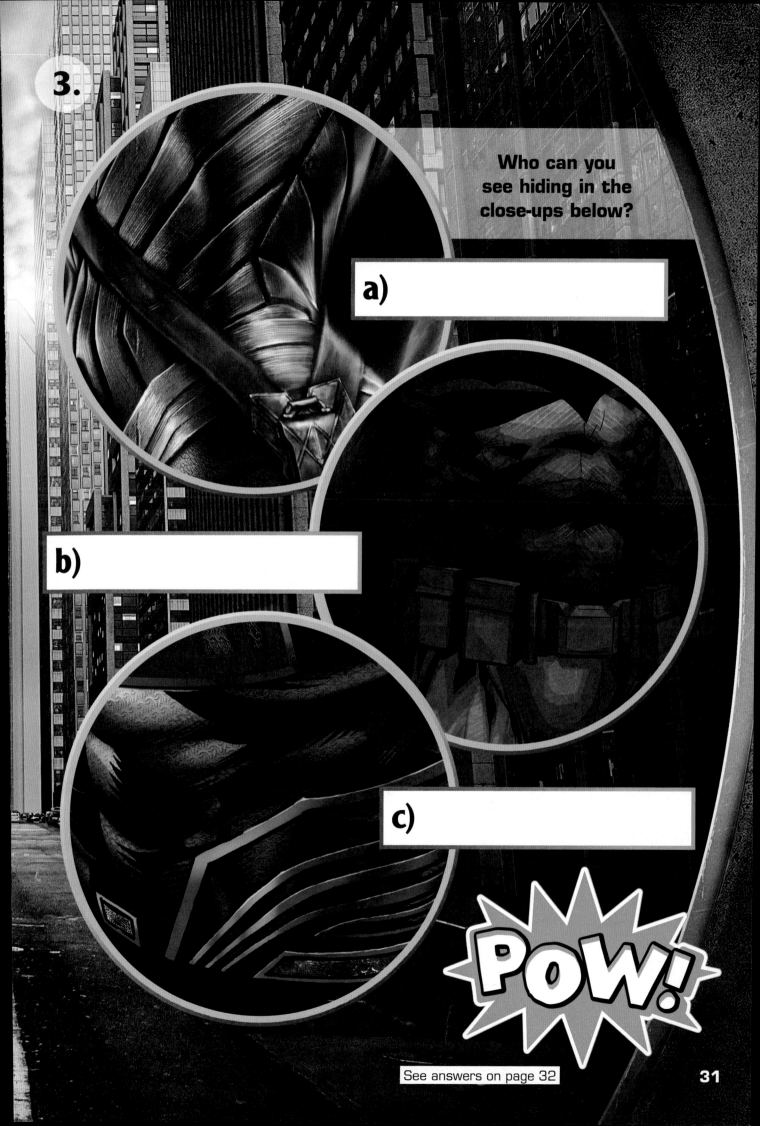

ANSWERS

Code phrase
SUPER HERO

Page 4

33 logos

Page 8

4

Page 9

a) Broken bridge: **super-strength**
b) Emergency: **super-speed**
c) Tall building: **flight**
d) Building collapse: **X-ray vision**

Page 14

2

Page 15

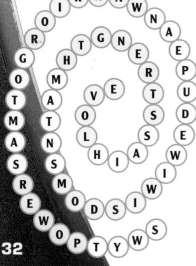

Page 18

H	E	R	O	R	V	I	G	I	L	A	N	T	E
E	G	O	T	U	H	A	H	M	C	H	E	R	O
R	N	A	M	O	W	R	E	D	N	O	W	V	I
O	S	U	P	I	E	R	R	M	A	N	I	E	G
C	R	B	A	V	T	M	O	N	A	N	L	L	R
N	A	E	L	A	H	I	A	L	I	E	N	I	O
A	B	A	H	S	E	M	L	E	X	L	U	B	H
M	T	C	L	A	R	K	K	E	N	T	A	O	T
T	M	O	B	E	O	O	I	L	E	T	N	M	U
A	D	N	P	E	R	R	H	E	R	O	O	T	L
B	R	U	C	E	W	A	Y	N	E	E	W	A	X
Q	S	C	H	L	A	R	M	K	R	N	Y	B	E
W	G	O	T	H	A	M	C	I	T	Y	G	L	L

HERO is hidden 8 times.

Page 19

Page 21

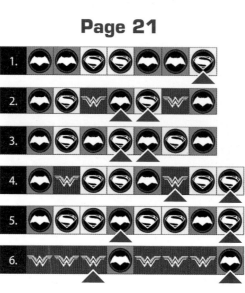

Page 23

```
        W           F
B R A V E S T       A
    R               S
S T R O N G E S T   T
    I       U       E
    O       A       S
S A V I O U R       T
            R
            D
            I
            A
            N
```

Page 26

Secret message:
Today is the day for truth.

Page 30

1.

2. 'Truth' appears 4 times
   in the grid.

Page 31

3. a) Wonder Woman
   b) Batman
   c) Superman

Page 20: CRIME FIGHTER PUZZLE

Page 21: SUPER HERO SEQUENCES

Page 30: SUDOKU